15-Minute Life Changers

GW00578183

A Way through Depression

Dr Ruth Fowke

Copyright © CWR 1995, 2002

First published 1995 as *New Perspectives, Towards the Light. A Way Through Depression*, by CWR. This edition published 2002 by CWR, Waverley Abbey House, Waverley Lane, Farnham, Surrey GU9 8EP.

Reprinted 2002, twice in 2003, 2005.

Concept development, editing, design and production by CWR.

Printed in England by Halstan.

ISBN 1-85345-212-2

Biography

Ruth Fowke was a Consultant General Psychiatrist for many years. She has long been interested in normal personality differences, and runs a variety of Myers-Briggs courses. On retiring from the NHS she trained in Spiritual Direction, and now also runs Quiet Days and Retreats.

Light at the End of the Tunnel

Read this page, and this booklet, only as far as you can read with comfort.
Do not try and read the whole page, or section, if that is too much for you.
Read on until one small crumb of comfort appears for you, then mull it over.
Meditate on that crumb and return to it as many times as you can.

Sometimes just being still is difficult. You may be restless, agitated and
distracted. That is your earthly housing which at the moment is sick. Accept
that, and direct your thoughts to God who sustains you. Do not fret because
you cannot keep focused on Him for long. At the moment you are unable to
focus on anything or anyone for any length of time.

When your thoughts wander just say the name Jesus, and recall one
attribute. Say Jesus – Saviour; Jesus – King; Jesus – Light; Jesus – Truth;
Jesus – friend of sinners, or whatever comes to your heart and mind.
That is all you need to do. Say that one thing again and again.

You do not need to feel different (although it would be nice if you felt better,
of course). You just need to call and He will be with you in your distress.

Believe that it will pass

It is also very hard to wait to come out of the depression that grips you
like a wet, grey blanket, but come out of it you will. It takes longer for some
than for others, but even if it takes a very long time, you will emerge from
the dark tunnel you are in. There is light at the end of the tunnel. Accept that
for the present you are in a tunnel. You may only be creeping along it, but
each passing moment takes you nearer to that light at the end.

Accept that you are depressed and do not force yourself to do more than
you can with comfort. Do only the essentials to keep you going. Anything
else you manage to get done is a bonus.

Believe that it will pass. If you have been depressed before, then remember that you did eventually come out of it. If this is your first experience of prolonged blackness, then take heart from those who have been there before, and have come through.

Look to God

Confirm your faith in God. You may feel despondent, even desperate that everything in you and around you seems black and hopeless. That is your human condition and, although it is hard to believe when you are deep in the tunnel, there is light and life outside.

Look beyond your immediate condition. Look to God who cares greatly for you. He cares because He is love. It is His nature to hold on to you when you cannot hold on to Him. Hold on to the fact that it is He who holds on to you, not you who hold on to Him.

For reflection and action:

- ACCEPT that you are depressed.
- CONCENTRATE on essentials only.
- BELIEVE this depression will pass.
- CONFIRM your faith in God.
- CALL on one of the names of Jesus.

Rest in the Shepherd's Arms

Being carried is just what you need right now. You probably have no energy to do anything much. Your concentration is likely to be poor and your interest in most things greatly diminished. None of this is your fault. Sickness is not sin. Part of this particular illness is that you are likely to feel that you are somehow to blame for your low state. You are no more so than if you had appendicitis, pneumonia or any other illness.

Relax. Allow God to carry you. It is hard to carry a struggling child. Stop struggling and trust the One who carries you.

Stop struggling

An experienced swimmer trusts himself to the water and is carried by it. He does just what is needed to keep afloat and to keep going. He lets the water hold him up. An inexperienced swimmer will flail his arms and legs frantically because he does not trust that the water really can hold him up. While he struggles he is fighting the very properties that would help him if only he would stop struggling so much.

Shepherds have an easier task of carrying sick or needy lambs when those lambs relax and just let themselves be borne along. They don't have to do anything else except to trust the shepherd and let him carry them. Lambs that struggle against the shepherd's grasp exhaust themselves and hamper the shepherd in his work of rescue. Those that leave off struggling conserve what energy they have. Co-operating with the shepherd is much more comfortable than kicking against him.

The Good Shepherd

Jesus is the Good Shepherd who leads His sheep. He never drives them on, but leads them gently. He goes at the pace of the slowest, the most infirm. He knows the characteristics of every individual sheep, and exactly what state each one is in at the moment. He sees that each one gets just what it needs. When any wander off and get caught in brambles, or stuck in impossible places, He does not abandon them. He goes after each one to rescue it, however long the rescue takes. He keeps calling to the lost sheep to comfort and reassure them, and He keeps on until each one is safely restored to the flock again. He is a tireless shepherd.

For reflection and action:

- *Cease struggling.*
- *Trust your shepherd.*
- *Listen for His voice.*
- *Allow yourself to be carried*

Firm on the Rock

That is just how depression feels – like being in a slimy pit, sinking in dark mud, with no way out. The fact is that there is something firm under the mud, there is a rock that will not keep shifting about. Knowing the rock is there does not make the mud any less muddy, but it does enable you to stop sinking any further. The mud remains cold, wet and clinging, but it no longer threatens you. It is unpleasant to be in, but you can obtain reassurance and the hope of rescue once your feet are planted on the rock.

The rock beneath the mud

When you focus your attention on the fact of the rock that is there beneath the mud, the unpleasantness of the mud you are standing in becomes more bearable. Yes, you are still in the mud and, yes, life will be much more pleasant when you get out of it, but when you concentrate on the solid fact of the solid rock, your feelings gradually become of less importance.

This does not happen all at once. Your feet search and squelch around and then, when they seem to land on something substantial, you are initially unsure whether it is rock or just a small stone that may slip away again, leaving you in the same mess as before. Only by trusting it with your weight can you prove that it is a reliable rock rather than a slippery stone. Only by gradually putting more weight on it, and finding that it does indeed support your full weight, can you prove that you are on good, solid, immovable rock.

Jesus told a parable about people who put His words into practice being like wise ones who build their houses on rock. Houses with such foundations will stand firm whatever the storms of life; they will not be washed away like those built on sand. The initial digging out is much harder

> **"He turned to me and heard my cry. He lifted me out of the slimy pit, out of the mud and mire; he set my feet on a rock and gave me a firm place to stand." Psalm 40:1, 2**

when you build on rock, but it is worth the effort. That rock will be unshaken whatever the weather outside. God's love and care endures forever, whatever the weather. It does not change with our particular passing state, or with the storms of life that we encounter.

Stand on God's Word

The only firm place to stand is on the Word of God. He promised Joshua, "*I will never leave you or forsake you.*" His character has not changed; He still promises never to leave us or forsake us. Although you may not feel Him to be very near, the fact is that He is the Rock beneath your feet, the mud and the mire will not engulf you.

Hang in there, even if it is with gritted teeth. Remember the rock on which you stand has more permanence and more validity than the mud you are in. The mud will eventually recede; the rock will remain.

For reflection and action:

- Trust the rock; it will last.
- Endure the mud; it will pass.
- Stand on the Word of God.

Gem Formation

We tend to think of darkness as undesirable, but there are treasures to be found there. The riches are hidden and need digging out. They are not found on the surface for all to see and for anyone to obtain, but are buried in the darkness underground. When they are dug out they may not initially look attractive or valuable. Probably they will seem dusty and dull. But after some attention is paid to them and they are polished up, we get sparkling precious and semi-precious stones which can only be formed in the dark, and often under pressure.

Diamonds are the best-known example, but rubies and sapphires too are only formed by the process of crushing and compression. When you are depressed you may feel utterly crushed as though you can take no more. Take heart. In the very pressure of being so crushed there is treasure being formed in you, riches waiting to be revealed, even though you cannot see, feel, or believe this to be true while the pressure is on.

Treasure out of darkness

The basic material of diamonds and of opals is colourless. It is the traces of impurities which give such gems their colours. At other times colour is given by light catching on minute cracks in the stone, so an apparent imperfection actually gives added value, added wealth, and wealth can come out of the seeming impurity and imperfection of depression.

Amber is a hard, translucent fossil resin from which gems are made. After the resin has been trapped for a very long time, it is slowly but surely turned into amber. When you are depressed it often feels as though you are caught in a trap from which you cannot escape. Take heart. Something better is being formed in you and will emerge in due time.

> **"I will give you the treasures of darkness, riches stored in secret places." Isaiah 45: 3**

You probably wish that you could escape the depression. But you can't; it is not your fault or your choosing, and it is not the fault of anyone else. It happens because of our human condition. Our humanity means that we are subject to a vast number of processes within us, any one of which can malfunction for a time.

Much great art is born out of suffering. Some of the great classical paintings, sculptures, musical compositions, poetry and some prose would not have become available in more pleasant circumstances. Some of our great hymns were written after a long period of depression, particularly some by William Cowper and John Newton. Beethoven, Darwin, Tolstoy, J.B. Phillips, Leslie Weatherhead, Tony Hancock and others all knew periods of depression which at the time seemed to impair their ability. Afterwards it was a source of inspiration to them, and through them to countless others.

Treasure actually comes out of the darkness. Not despite the darkness, but out of the very blackness itself.

For reflection and action:

- Darkness deepens character and value.
- Treasure comes out of darkness, not despite it.
- Apparent imperfections add to the value of many real gems.
- Suffering can inspire.

Not Forgotten

It is natural to ask these questions. Why am I depressed? Why me? And why now? What have I done wrong? Any one of us is liable to react at some time with some degree of low spirits, or depression. Whether or not we become deeply depressed for a prolonged time will depend on the interplay of our genetic make-up, our personality and the life events we encounter along the way.

We inherit our genes and are not responsible for them, although we are responsible to some degree for how we manage or mismanage what we are made of.

One day as they were passing a blind man the disciples of Jesus asked him who had sinned, the man or his parents, that he was born blind. Jesus replied that neither the man nor his parents had sinned, but that this had happened so that the work of God might be displayed in his life. In keeping with their generation and upbringing the disciples assumed that sin must be the cause of the problem of this particular individual. Like them, we must be careful not to make assumptions and over-quick judgements on ourselves or on others. We must guard against being judgemental, speculative and presumptive about the cause of our distress. We need to concentrate instead on God Himself, on His majesty and on His compassion.

He will never leave you

Over and over again He promises to be with us in our distress. He does not promise that our lives will be trouble-free or disease-free. He does most emphatically promise that no matter what our circumstances and our distress, He will not forget us or desert us. "*Can a mother forget the baby at her breast and have no compassion on the child she has borne? Though she may forget, I will not forget you*" (Isaiah 49:15).

A mother feels the distress of her child and gives him the comfort of her presence. Whether or not she can remove the problem and make it better there and then, she will be with her child in his distress. God is like that mother to us, and more. He is our source of life as well as our solace in difficult times and He will always come when we call out for Him.

Put your hope in God

Trying to deny or to hide your depression will only increase your distress. The psalmist in the verse for today was able to say "*My soul is downcast within me.*" He admitted the state he was in, and then he was able to go on and say to his own soul "*Put your hope in God, for I will yet praise him, my Saviour and my God.*"

For reflection and action:

- Admit that you are down.
- Praise God for who He is.
- Say aloud His promise "I will not forget you."

Come ... Rest ... Learn

This is surely an invitation for all who are depressed! Weariness of mind occurs early on in depression. It is likely to be followed by lethargy, and later by a marked physical tiredness. Accompanying this is often an inability to think with one's accustomed clarity and speed. The ordinary affairs of life become distorted and exaggerated. They begin to look formidable and soon become a burden.

Jesus shoulders our burdens

Jesus promises rest for the weary and burdened, but it is not the "rest" of giving up and doing nothing. It is the rest of doing what one is capable of, doing it in step with Him, walking alongside Him, and letting Him be the pacesetter. He takes the lead, and as He leads so He shoulders the burdens.

Some people find it helpful to visualise their burdens in their mind's eye, and then to find a way of graphically giving them over to the Lord. Some may see themselves approaching Jesus as He stands in front of the cross, and kneeling as they lay their burdens one by one at His feet. Others may put their burdens into a cloth which they then tie up, hand the whole bundle over and watch Jesus dispose of it in whatever way He chooses. Yet others find it helpful in their imagination to name their burdens as they place them in a box which they give to Jesus and watch as He throws it behind the cross, or into a deep sea – putting up a "No fishing here" sign as He does so.

Being yoked to Jesus, pulling with Him and not against Him, means learning the ropes of living from Him. This entails asking Him each day what He wants to teach that day. It means living one day at a time, but living it with Him.

> **"Come to me, all you who are weary and burdened, and I will give you rest. Take my yoke upon you, and learn from me ... My yoke is easy and my burden is light." Matthew 11:28–30**

He is never in a rush, and He never overloads us. In one of His teaching sermons with His disciples He said, *"I have much more to say to you, more than you can now bear"* (John 16:12). He knows our load-bearing capacity, our individual Plimsoll line, and He never exceeds it.

Tune in to His presence

Jesus never did anything in His own strength, He was always conscious of His Father's presence with Him, and the Father's purpose for His life. He said, *"By myself I can do nothing ... I seek not to please myself but him who sent me ... I do nothing on my own ..."* (John 5:30; 8:28).

We learn from Him by constantly tuning in and re-tuning to His presence at many moments through the day. Brother Lawrence so practised this tuning-in process that he was able to claim, "The time of business does not with me differ from the time of prayer; and in the noise and clutter of my kitchen, while several persons are at the same time calling for different things, I possess God in as great tranquillity as if I were upon my knees at prayer."

For reflection and action:

- Hand your burdens over to Jesus every day.
- Take his yoke, and walk in step with Him.
- Keep re-tuning to His presence with you and in you.

Simplify to Survive

It is a very good principle never to reverse in depression any good and right decision made before the depression struck. Self-doubt creeps in as part of the depression and the person's judgement is often distorted about many things. This is not a good time to be making important decisions, and it is a very poor time to change those already made.

While the depression lasts it is wise to keep your life as simple as possible. Do the things that are necessary just to keep ticking over, but do not take on anything extra during this time. There is no need to fear that you will never pick up the threads of a busy life again. You will be well able to do so when you recover, as recover you will. Right now your emphasis needs to be on survival, and that probably requires some simplification of your usual lifestyle.

Save your energy

It may be prudent to cut down on activities that are not strictly necessary, and on anything which requires you to make a decision. It is usual to find that everyday decisions are now hard to make, even those that previously you took in your stride. Now the little things become enormous and consume a great deal of your energy. Save your effort for those things that really are essential, and prune out the unimportant, and the less important ones.

Plants grow better and are more fruitful after their current size and activity has been reduced, even drastically reduced, by proper pruning. Remember that Jesus Himself is the life-giving vine, and His Father (and ours) is the gardener who trims clean every fruitful branch in order that it

> **"Let your eyes look straight ahead . . . and take only ways that are firm. Do not swerve to the right or the left." Proverbs 4:25–27**

can eventually become even more fruitful. Depression can result in an enforced pruning, so co-operate with the process and let some of the branches drop away. Do not cling to all your accustomed activities.

Letting go

Letting go can be a hard, even agonising, thing to do. Since it requires making some decisions, you will probably need the help of a trusted friend as you set about temporarily shedding some of your usual responsibilities and activities. Having made some decisions about simplifying your life in order to conserve your energy for the most essential things, stick to those decisions. Do not even entertain the idea of going back on them, or modifying them. Don't swerve one way or the other. Keep going straight ahead. Let the eyes of your heart, mind and will look only straight ahead.

Just to keep going is your task for the moment. It is important to live one day at a time, and to take only ways that are tried and tested. Anything new and unfamiliar is likely to add to your distress and difficulties. Stick to the ways and paths that are firm, and you will find them to be helpful and supportive.

For reflection and action:

* Stick to your decisions.
* Keep your life simple.
* Prune out non-essential activities and responsibilities.

The Rock of Refreshment

Depression takes the colour out of life, sometimes literally as well as metaphorically. Someone told me quite factually and without self-pity, "I know daffodils are yellow, but this year they all look grey to me." He himself did not look very different to his friends, but his perception of the world around him was altered by the illness.

His reception of the signals he received had become distorted and jumbled – the sort of thing that happens when a colour TV suddenly transmits only black and white, or the picture is misrepresented in some other way. There is a technical fault somewhere between the source and the reception of the picture.

It was not only his perception that was affected. His ability to function to his normal level and at his normal speed was reduced and he had nothing in reserve to fall back on. His tank was empty and he needed help. He came and asked for it, and in time he recovered. Medical help in depression is very important, and should always be sought. Spiritual issues must also be considered alongside medical help.

A friend tells me that some years ago while working in a foreign country it was all she could do just to keep going. One day she was trekking on foot to another village and stopped to rest in a wide river bed that was absolutely dry. There were grey boulders and grey stones and grey pebbles and she realised that that was exactly how she was feeling. She not only felt totally dried up and dried out, but she also realised all the colour had drained out of her life.

The Rock of our salvation

She sat and let that awareness sink in. Slowly she also became aware of the rock on which she was sitting. It was strong and stable amongst all the loose debris of that dried-up river bed. She began to associate this strong, supportive rock with Christ who is the Rock of our salvation. She realised that He is indeed her bedrock. He is all she had. She had absolutely no other resources to draw on, she was so utterly dried-up.

She continued to sit there, reflecting on Christ her Rock, until she was physically and spiritually refreshed enough to continue on her way. The scenery around her had not changed, it was still grey and dry. Her life situation had not changed and she herself still felt dried-up. But by looking to Christ her Rock, and drawing strength from Him, she was able to carry on.

She was helped by two things that happened almost simultaneously. She became aware of her condition, and her attention turned away from herself to God, her Rock. She did not have it within her to do anything for herself. She just realised anew her utter, total dependence on God, and she was refreshed. She relied fully on God, and found Him fully reliable.

For reflection and action:

- *Rest on Christ, your Rock.*
- *Draw your strength from Him.*
- *Seek medical help also.*

Be Kind to Yourself

Watch your clothing! It is very easy for a depressed person to increase their depression by being slovenly, wearing stained or torn clothing, not bothering to mop up spills – or just not bothering. When some care is taken with dressing it may still have a negative effect. If what is chosen is of nondescript colour and shape, presenting a drab and dreary appearance, then this reinforces the depression. Of course that is just how a depressed person does feel, and dressing the opposite of what you feel can begin to reverse the prevailing mood.

Don't be hard on yourself

We are told to clothe ourselves with compassion and kindness. This means of course that we must have as much compassion for, and be as kind to, ourselves as we are towards others. People who are depressed are so often hard on themselves, harder on themselves than they would be to anyone else. Frequently they feel unworthy of the little kindnesses and the consideration that is due to everyone. The verse for today does not go on to say " ... except when you are depressed", and that addendum is not found anywhere else in Scripture either.

To feel worthless and useless is part of the whole spectrum of a depressive illness. It is important therefore to watch out for and to correct any tendency to regard yourself as somehow outside the good things, especially the promises and blessings contained in Scripture. You may need to ask trusted friends to gently challenge you when they detect you falling into this familiar trap.

Forgiveness

Our Colossians passage goes on to say, "*Bear with each other and forgive whatever grievances you may have against one another*" (v.13). Forgiveness is so important in maintaining healthy relationships. It keeps us in a right relationship with God, with one another – and with ourselves.

Sometimes the inability, or unwillingness, to forgive another may be a contributory factor in either causing or prolonging depression. When I was in clinical practice the words that most dismayed me were along the lines, "I will never forgive ...", for they seemed to convey a closed mind coupled with a closed heart.

We are urged to forgive as the Lord has forgiven us. It certainly helps us to obey this when we can see our unforgiveness, whether that is of ourselves or of others, in the light of Jesus' total forgiveness of us. Please note that we are expected to forgive ourselves, as well as others. If Jesus can and does forgive us, should we dare to do otherwise?

Sometimes people who are deeply depressed believe themselves to be completely beyond forgiveness by anyone, including Jesus. When a person is unable to accept that the Scriptures on this subject could possibly extend to himself, then he is in need of urgent medical as well as pastoral help.

For reflection and action:

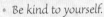

- Be kind to yourself.
- Wear something to cheer yourself (and others) up.
- Forgive yourself. If you can't, get medical help now.

Held

One of the hallmarks of depression is a sense of alienation, of being cut off from other people, of being outside the enjoyment and unable to join in. You feel isolated because the illness has temporarily robbed you of your ability to resonate with the wavelength of those around you. You are likely to feel utterly alone and forlorn in a room full of friends. They talk and laugh together but you are now an onlooker, unable to join in as once you would have done.

Sometimes it seems as if life in general, and your friends in particular, are passing you by. You may feel they have deserted you because they are busy with their own affairs and you are no longer able to contribute. It is most alarming to feel so alone and alienated, even though you would probably be agitated and bothered by people if they did call round.

He is always with you

Take heart. There is one who will never ever leave you or forsake you. He is always near to you and always available for you. The psalmist was able to write of his sense of God's presence in a very personal way when he wrote:

> ... *you hold me by my right hand.*
> *You guide me with your counsel,*
>   *and afterwards you will take me into glory ...*
> *My flesh and my heart may fail,*
>   *but God is the strength of my heart*
>   *and my portion for ever.* (Psalm 73:23, 24, 26)

He holds you by the hand

I remember during one rather bleak time travelling to be with some special friends who knew my situation. They were going to meet me at the international airport of a country they were just passing through and take me on to their home. There was chaos at Heathrow, with many flights cancelled due to a strike elsewhere, and I had no means of contacting them as they were in transit. The hall was packed tight with delayed and despondent travellers, yet I had a strong sense of being led by the hand, of having my hand held by my heavenly Father who had the whole matter under control. My flight was one of the few to get away that day, it was called on time and I almost danced down the gangway like a small child, secure with my hand in that of my Father.

For reflection and action:

- *God is with you. He holds your right hand.*
- *He will never, ever, leave you.*
- *God is your strength – especially when you have none of your own.*

To Fall is to Learn

The desire to keep going, to do a good job and not to fall down or fail is strong in most of us. Usually this desire is our ally, but like so many things it can become distorted when a person is depressed. When it becomes a desire to do things absolutely right, to achieve impossible standards, it is a handicap, not a help to us. It is as though people secretly say to themselves something like, "If I can't be sure that I will get it absolutely and completely right then I won't do it at all." They become paralysed by their own perfectionism.

The "good enough" principle

People suffering from the paralysis of perfectionism need to learn, and to practise, the principle of the "good enough". This means that they will say to themselves something like: "Even though I know I cannot do a perfect job, I will make sure that what I do is a good enough job." They will get things done because they accept that few things can be done absolutely perfectly.

Being satisfied with the "good enough" does not mean poor standards, but adequate standards. It cannot be used as an excuse for poor, slipshod work. The "good enough" principle ensures that whatever is done is neither too much nor too little, but just right to achieve the desired goal.

It is right to have high standards, but they must be achievable. In horse show-jumping the final jump-off is sometimes made steadily higher until some horses know it is beyond them and they refuse to tackle it. A wise rider does not force them into another attempt – horse sense prevails.

The horse has not failed. The task that was set was too much. It is important to recognise that failure is not the end. It may be the end of this attempt, this opportunity, this route to go down, but it is not the end of me.

> **"If the Lord delights in a man's way, he makes his steps firm; though he stumble, he will not fall, for the Lord upholds him with his hand."**
> **Psalm 37:23, 24**

If you fall it isn't fatal

I have found the various translations of Psalm 37 verse 24 helpful when I have put off attempting something for fear that I will fail in my endeavour. Best of all for me is *"If they fall it isn't fatal, for the Lord holds them with his hand"* (Living Bible). Others are: *"Though he fall, he shall not be utterly cast down, for the Lord grasps his hand in support and upholds him"* (Amplified); *"When he trips he is not thrown sprawling, since Yahweh supports him by the hand"* (Jerusalem); *"Though he may fall, he will not go headlong, for the Lord grasps him by the hand"* (NEB); *"If they fall, they will not stay down, because the Lord will help them up"* (GNB).

An infant cannot learn to walk without falling many times; it is part of the learning process. As we get older and more skilled we fall less often, but in this life we cannot expect never to trip up.

It's all right to fall – He is there to catch you. He will grasp you, support you, hold you and help you up.

For reflection and action:

- Learn and practise the principle of "good enough".
- Check that your standards are achievable.
- Remind yourself it's OK to fall – the Lord will pick you up and get you going again.

The End is the Beginning

Now, in depression, is the time to trust God that by His grace He really will be sufficient for your needs. He is great enough and caring enough to meet all your needs. He has more than enough resources, He has ample resources to meet your needs however long they continue.

Find strength in the Lord

It is a paradox that *"When I am weak, then I am strong,"* as Paul goes on to say in the passage for consideration today (v.10). Sometimes it is only when I am weak that God really has a chance to be God in my life. Only when I let go of my ability and my strength is there a chance for Him to show what He wants to do.

All the time I am trying to manage, to get by, to keep going, I am relying on my own strength and not on Him. When I am strong, or believing that I am strong, or am trying to be strong, then God does not get a chance to be strong for me and in me. He longs to show me His gentle strength and to exercise it on my behalf.

Only when I come to the end of my tether do I really find out who is at the other end. God is there, quietly and patiently holding on. I do not have to cling on with grim determination, for He is lovingly and firmly doing the holding.

That is where my strength lies – not in me, or my abilities, or my training, but in Him. Only when I acknowledge that I can do nothing, can He begin to do something. When I admit that I have come to the end of myself then His life can begin to grow in me.

Sometimes our lives are so full of activity that we lose touch with our inner selves, the core of our being, that created being who relates to the

Creator. It is easy to become so busy that we turn into human doings, instead of being human beings. Depression brings us to an end of ourselves, and if we turn, or return, to God He will hold us and uphold us. His grace will be sufficient.

God's in there with you

Because depression brings us to an end of ourselves, and painfully shows as our inability to continue on our own, it can be the beginning of spiritual awakening. Turning our attention away from ourselves and on to God, and finding Him incarnate in the depressive morass, we can begin to build on this relationship. We find Him in the morass, not waiting until we climb out of it.

God did not speak to Elijah in the whirlwind, or through the earthquake, or the fire that followed, but in a gentle whisper. It is in quietness and trust that our true strength lies.

For reflection and action:

- Let go of things you cling to.
- When you're at the end of your tether, God is at the other end.
- You are a human being, not a human doing.

Modest Changes

Depressed people often feel deserted – especially by God. This sense of distance is a familiar part of the illness. Some people experience others close to them as having become remote, unapproachable, almost in another world. When this is a generalised perception it has to be recognised as part of the overall condition. It does not necessarily indicate that the individual is out of sorts in the spiritual realm. The illness temporarily clouds his spiritual grasp, but not the underlying reality. To regard depression as a specifically spiritual malady only increases the feeling of guilt and blame. In any individual it may, or may not, have a spiritual component.

Many types of depression

Depression is such an umbrella word. Many different conditions shelter beneath its covering span. Because of this the answer, if there is one, to the question about why it has occurred, or recurred, will differ for each person.

All of us know days of being a bit down, with or without a readily recognisable reason. Then there's the down of disappointment which may sometimes be so much more than a passing blip on our chart of emotional well-being. Some people are bothered, even depressed, when for a time life seems disordered, out of control and ambiguous, for they need an ordered, structured and predictable life to function well. Others are just the opposite. They become depressed when life is too predictable because they need variety and change to keep them going. Still others become depressed when life has lost its prime purpose and meaning for them. For yet others it may be when life seems illogical or has lost its challenge, that they become down, because they need something to strive for.

For all of these people depression serves either to get them back on their accustomed course, or sets them examining their goals and habitual actions so that they begin to make changes appropriate to their current situation.

Spiritual nourishment

Some of these changes may need to be in the area of spiritual nourishment. If they have only employed the prayer of asking, of intercession and petition, perhaps the time has come for more listening to and waiting receptively on God. Learning to meditate on Scripture, rather than always reading it for information, could be just what is needed at this time.

What is helpful at one stage of our life's journey may be less so at another. God is not hiding Himself in disapproval of those who are depressed. Sometimes He does make Himself less evident for a time in order to stimulate us to seek Him in fresh ways. People who are depressed are most likely to be helped by becoming both less talkative and more simple in their times of prayer. Just a few lines read with relish are more nourishing than a whole chapter read with dogged determination but little meaning.

For reflection and action:

- Your understanding may be clouded; the reality of God remains.
- Review your goals in life.
- Be less talkative and more simple in prayer.

Winter Will Pass

Depression is like winter, endless and cheerless and cold. There is neither present comfort nor the prospect of anything different, anything better on the horizon. When it is always winter and never Christmas there is no relief to look forward to.

What is needed is an interruption that enables you to carry on. A break in routine helps you to face the remaining days of winter, knowing that the worst is over. The longest night has passed for this year, winter is slowly on the wane and spring will surely follow, but we need the break, the hope, of Christmas to cope with the long winter.

Have you got a log-jam?

Sometimes a different sort of break is called for. In some but not all types of depression the necessary break that heralds the worst is over seems to be the shifting of one particularly obstructive attitude. In countries where they float logs down rivers to the saw mills, loggers are employed to watch out for log-jams, and they are very skilled at getting the jammed log free. Sometimes the entire flow of logs has been held up because just one got jammed and so nothing else can move. Behind that one awkwardly placed log all the others pile up, unable to continue their journey. Nothing moves. The flow of life has stopped.

When you seem to be stuck in depression and you feel as if your life has come to a standstill, look for the log in your life that has got jammed. It is likely to be some hidden attitude towards another person, rather than an event or circumstance external to you, that is holding back the flow of your life. Bring the situation to God. Just tell Him you are in a jam. Acknowledge the problem, ask for help and await the prod that will set you free.

> **"It is winter in Narnia, and has been for ever so long ...
> Always winter and never Christmas."**
> *The Lion, the Witch and the Wardrobe*, **C. S. Lewis**

Talk it out with the Lord

When the Holy Spirit brings into your awareness some attitude that might be contributing to, even causing, your depression, He will only do so in love, and for your healing. Talk to Him about your feelings and your battles. If you feel let down, passed over, neglected, undervalued or devalued, then have a conversation with Him about exactly how you feel. No holds barred.

If you find you have been harbouring a hitherto unacknowledged sense of betrayal, or anger, or you are clinging on to some hurt, then talk this out with the Lord of your life. The situation will take on a totally different perspective as you talk it through.

Is there something, which means someone, you are as yet unable to really forgive? Be open about your difficulties in this area. Examine the situation and ask for grace to begin to let go of the hurt or whatever you find is causing the log-jam, in order that healing may flow in, and your life may begin to flow freely again.

For reflection and action:

- Take a break; have a treat.
- Look for the log that may be holding up the flow of life.
- Pray out your feelings; no holds barred.

Back to Basics

Wanting to run away, to just give up, is a common feature in depression. When there is no let up in the whole constellation of symptoms that drag one down, and no lightening of the load, many people experience the desire to crawl away and hide. They want to hide from themselves, and from others, until the awfulness, the dread, the blackness, the debilitating gloom begins to lift.

Running from God

Sometimes people retain the sense of their faith during this phase, and sometimes they seem to lose it for a while. Those who do retain a sense of God's presence may even wish that they did not, that they could forget Him or shrug Him off, or run away from Him. For some this is because the mental distortion which is often such a part of depression has temporarily affected how and what they think about God. The illness does not, of course, affect how God regards them, His love and His whole character are unchanging. When they recover from their illness their concept of God will also recover.

For others the wish to run away may be because deep down their basic idea of the nature of God has always been incomplete. They may have an intellectual appreciation of God the Creator, but an emotional attachment that remains infantile. In their heart of hearts they may still think of God as a sort of Father Christmas, there to give them good things if they behave well and ask nicely and don't upset Him. Or they may confuse God the Father with some memories of an angry, unjust parent. Their understanding of God, when it is teased out, may consist largely of images of the man with a big stick, waiting to strike or of someone who is fickle and unreliable.

If depression brings to light any such notions, then something good will come out of the experience. When someone recognises that their understanding of God has been false or incomplete, they can set about the process of acquiring a more mature and biblical concept.

When plagued with depression we need to go back to basics. As our psalm for today puts it, "*I call as my heart grows faint; lead me to the rock that is higher than I.*" Rest on the rock.

Nothing can shake God's love for you

Recall the fact that "*The Lord is compassionate and gracious, slow to anger, abounding in love*" (Psalm 103:8). His very nature is love. He does not just tolerate us or love us in some abstract way; He abounds, He overflows with love. There are times when it is right that we act in response to this love, when we do things for Him and with Him because of His love for us. But there are also times when we need to stop doing, and be content with just being. Being in His presence, resting in and on His love, delighting to be in its shade. Quietly remind yourself that He says, "*Though the mountains be shaken and the hills be removed, yet my unfailing love for you will not be shaken*" (Isaiah 54:10).

For reflection and action:

* Illness clouds the view, not the reality.
* Your images of God may need updating.
* God's love is unfailing, and unshakeable.

Escape Road

While you wait for your depression to lift, remember that God is in control even of that. He will see that it is not greater and does not last longer than you, with His help, can bear. He does provide a way out, and that reminds me of those short escape roads that are provided at intervals down very steep hills. I have come across them approaching Lynmouth in north Devon. They are a way of coping, an alternative to having a crash. They are angled uphill and their surface is deep sand. If your brakes don't hold and your gears fail, those roads of sand are guaranteed to bring your runaway car under control. They are a way out of a predicament.

When you're tempted to give up

When life feels out of control and you are tempted to give up, remember that Jesus was tempted that way too. He coped by looking beyond His present problem to the deeper, eternal purpose of God. In our turn we can cope when we fix our eyes on Jesus, "*the author and perfecter of our faith, who for the joy set before him endured the cross, scorning its shame, and sat down at the right hand of the throne of God. Consider him ... so that you will not grow weary and lose heart*" (Hebrews 12:2–3).

Because He stuck it out to the end so can we, by His grace and with His strength, hang on when the going is tough. He is our escape road. Stick it out with Him until relief comes, as come it will.

The apostle Paul was able to write about being "*Hard pressed on every side but not crushed; perplexed, but not in despair; persecuted but not abandoned; struck down but not destroyed ... we do not lose heart*" (2 Corinthians 4:8–9, 16). He was certainly writing from personal experience of enduring trials and much suffering when he made that bold assertion that "*you will not be tempted beyond what you can bear*". That is not theory, it is the voice of experience.

> "God is faithful; he will not let you be tempted beyond what you can bear. But when you are tempted, he will also provide a way out so that you can stand up under it." 1 Corinthians 10:13

Keep your eyes on Jesus

He did not have an extraordinary physique, nor was he naturally a particularly brave or fearless person. Imprisoned, beaten, stoned and left for dead; robbed, cold and hungry, and deserted by friends, he despaired of life. In his despair he looked to Jesus and was given the ability to hang on when the going was exceedingly tough. He endured only because he knew Jesus was his escape road, always at hand when the need arose.

For reflection and action:

- *Keep your eyes on Jesus. He is your escape road. You will not crash.*
- *"You will not be tempted beyond what you can bear."*

Endurance

In depression there is often a feeling of sinking, even drowning. There is a sense of getting lower and weaker, and being quite unable to lift oneself out of the slough of despond. If this happens to you, do not struggle. Simply remember that Jesus is right there beside you. He is there with you in the depression that threatens to overcome you; but it won't. You will not be overwhelmed, for He is with you.

You are not alone

Suffering is always tough, and to suffer alone is almost unendurable. Fortunately God has said: *"Never will I leave you; never will I forsake you"* (Hebrews 13:5). We may lose the sense of His nearness, but the fact of His presence does not depend on our awareness of it. His presence is guaranteed by His nature, His very character and by His promises to us.

He promises to be with us, whatever our health, whatever our difficulties, whatever our suffering. We do not know the answer to the "whys" about suffering. We do not know why some go through it and others do not. What we do know is that God will never abandon us, never leave us to bear our suffering alone.

Of course we would like the problem, the dis-ease, to be cleared up and removed from us, but that is not the promise. The deal is that God will be with us as we soldier on. He is alongside us in the pain, the confusion, the hopelessness, the wretchedness. We are assured that *"a bruised reed he will not break, and a smouldering wick he will not snuff out"* (Isaiah 42:3).

He will never let you go

Take heart that the depression will not snuff you out. You are far too precious to God. He will not let go of you, He will not let you slip under.

> **"When you pass through the waters, I will be with you; and when you walk through the fire, you will not be burned; the flames will not set you ablaze." Isaiah 43:2.**

You are actually engraved on the palm of His hand (Isaiah 49:16) and so have become a part of Him. Ineradicable. Precious. Treasured. Beloved. Honoured.

You are treasured because of your very frailty, not in spite of it. "*We have this treasure in jars of clay to show that this all-surpassing power is from God and not from us*" (2 Corinthians 4:7). We are breakable, it is in our nature. God is compassionate, it is in His nature.

Endurance is called for, and what an example we have in Jesus who endured the cross.

We cannot drum up endurance from our own resources, we must rely on our Lord. Paul urged the younger man Timothy to "*be strong in the grace that is in Christ Jesus*" (2 Timothy 2:1). That grace is available to help you to be strong and to endure. Ask for it. Receive it. Rest in it. He will give it. He will hold you, and uphold you.

For reflection and action:

- You are engraved on the palm of God's hand.
- He will never leave you or forsake you.
- You may be a clay jar – but you hold great treasure.

Anchored

Oh the utter hopelessness of the psalmist's words! Because depression may run on into months, in extreme cases even years, the sufferer not unnaturally loses hope of recovery. Everything is terrible right now, and as the days and weeks drag on, the future appears to hold no better prospect. There seems little point in making any effort any more and the tendency is to just give up.

The gift of hope

When we consider giving up on life we are also, if we dare to admit it, giving up on God who now seems so remote, unreachable and apparently uncaring. We cannot manufacture hope for ourselves, but we can receive it. It is a gift which we can look for, and long for, and request. Having asked, we need to believe we will receive. It is rather like being in a foreign country and knowing that a special friend has written to us, but the letter has not yet arrived. We keep looking out for it. Sometimes we fear it has gone astray, but we still keep watching and waiting. And then one day it comes, that longed-for letter.

All the way through the Bible we see that God is a God who gives hope to His people in a whole variety of tough situations. He gives hope in times of national disaster and decline, and in personal dilemmas also. And not just a faint glimmer of hope either, but a sure, steady beacon. He Himself is the God of hope. Paul writes to the Romans, "*May the God of hope fill you with all joy and peace as you trust in him, so that you may overflow with hope by the power of the Holy Spirit*" (Romans 15:13).

When He was dying on the cross Jesus Himself knew, and bore on our behalf, the utter hopelessness of being abandoned. He was for a time totally forsaken by God, in order that we would never need to suffer the same fate.

For the first and only time in His life He was completely on His own. As He hung on the cross He cried out in bitter agony, agony of spirit and of body. Those words of Psalm 22 with which we began today's meditation were wrung from His lips, and then His life on earth ended.

An anchor for the soul

As He died the veil of the temple was torn in two, split from the top to the bottom. That veil had always symbolised a limitation on access to God, but now that limitation has been withdrawn and we have direct access to the God of hope.

"We have this hope as an anchor for the soul, firm and secure. It enters the inner sanctuary behind the curtain, where Jesus, who went before us, has entered on our behalf" (Hebrews 6:19–20).

In depression the sky is black, the sea is rough, but that anchor will hold.

For reflection and action:

- Ask – expect – receive the gift of hope.
- Place your trust in Jesus, who overcame.
- Let your anchor hold you firm.

Smouldering Embers

It is not necessarily true that because you are depressed you must be harbouring hidden anger, but that is one factor among several that merits consideration. When there is an element of anger it will delay full resolution of the depression until it is dealt with.

Anger of itself is not sin. It is a neutral energy. How I express my anger will determine whether it becomes sinful or not. Not expressing anger can actually be a sin of omission. Failing to speak out can be a disservice to others, and harmful to myself.

Recognising anger

The crucial factors are to express anger to the right person, at a suitable time, and in an appropriate way. I must be aware of my anger in order to deal with it in an acceptable, healthy way, without also sinning. If I deny or disown my anger there is a real danger that it will erupt at the wrong people, at an inappropriate time and in an unacceptable manner. Alternatively, if it never surfaces it may be turned in on myself and manifest itself as depression.

Since anger is energy, it has to be discharged somewhere, somehow. Ideally that energy will be directed towards bringing about a remedial change in the causal situation. When it is neither recognised nor expressed in any way it does not just cease to exist. Unless dealt with, it will smoulder on, undetected perhaps for years, until something apparently quite unconnected fans the embers. It may then ignite inappropriately, giving rise to irritability, caustic comments or cynicism. Happily, it can also be used creatively, through art, drama or other experiences.

As well as anger there may be other feelings. Fear, anxiety and some excitement are likely to chase each other in quick succession. Try to name each emotion you are aware of. Accept them non-judgementally, so that you can deal with the underlying attitude. Remember that acceptance does not imply approval, it merely recognises and acknowledges the fact of existence.

Pray for honesty and boldness to face whatever feelings and memories you may have had to lock away. With God's help you can unlock the cellar and release the energy that is trapped there.

Having recognised and utilised your anger, be sure not to let it build up again. Allow yourself to be aware when you are angry, what you are angry about and who you are angry with so that you can channel the energy into useful action at a suitable time.

"*Do not let the sun go down while you are still angry*" (Ephesians 4:26). This is a daily discipline. Having recognised that I am angry I then have to decide how to handle the variety of issues involved. My attitudes have to be faced honestly and prayerfully, before sundown. When others are involved it may not be appropriate to take immediate action, but acknowledging to myself that there is an issue to deal with later will help me to prevent my anger leading me into sin now.

For reflection and action:

* Anger is energy. Use it wisely
* Anger is not sin. Be careful how you express it, though.
* Acceptance that you are angry does not necessarily imply approval.

One Step at a Time

There is a Chinese proverb which reminds us that even the longest journey begins with the first step. When the journey before you seems too long, too arduous or too difficult, take your eye off the distant goal and focus on an intermediate landmark instead. When the ultimate destination seems unattainable, make for resting stops along the way.

When it seems too hard

In their journeys the people of Israel often came across seemingly impossible barriers. They found that God is apt to provide rather different solutions to apparently similar problems encountered at different times by different groups. He held up the Red Sea so the entire people of Israel could leave Egypt, crossing quickly on dry ground. Later, when Joshua led nine and a half of the twelve tribes across the barrier of the River Jordan, it continued to flow right up to the moment when the feet of the priests carrying the ark of the Lord actually stepped into the water. They had to get their feet wet, and to exercise very considerable faith in their leader and in their God.

Centuries later Isaiah foretold a different solution. This time the obstacle to progress, and to freedom, was the Euphrates river. It would not be held back en masse but would be broken up "*into seven streams so that men can cross over in sandals*" (Isaiah 11:15). They would be able to ford each of the seven streams in turn, and on the intervening land they would have the opportunity to rest and refresh themselves before tackling the next one. They could look back on their achievement so far and say, "With God's help we've crossed one safely, now let's take one more, then we'll pause again." Looking at all seven barriers to progress was enough to prevent them from ever setting out, but by taking one at a time the prospect became more manageable, as it will for you.

> " ... a highway for our God ... the rough ground shall become level, the rugged places a plain." Isaiah 40:3, 4

Most of us long for the "all at once" Red Sea sort of solution to our difficulties, but that is not always God's chosen way. Sometimes He does do a gracious act of healing all on one occasion. At other times He seems to offer us a way more like crossing the great Euphrates in seven gradual stages. Whichever way is offered to us, we have to step out in obedience and faith that there will be a highway there. We have to take the first step, and then the next step.

One step at a time

Cope with your depression one day at a time. Tackle the urgent, the next task, only. Do not look at any tasks beyond the immediate next step. Do not look far into the future, but do encourage yourself by seeing the bit of progress you have already made. Even if it is only to get up out of bed, and get washed and dressed when you'd rather give up and lie in. You have taken the first step necessary for today. Do not discourage yourself with all that still remains to be done. Instead, encourage yourself with what you have managed to do. That's great.

For reflection and action:

* Focus on the next stage, not the ultimate goal.
* Take one step at a time.
* Encourage yourself by acknowledging progress already made.

Sandhills and Seasons

There is a right time for everything, including resting. In some seasons of life there seems to be little going on, and at others there is great activity. So it is in depression; life and growth continue although sometimes there is no sign of any activity. You get days when you can do a little and days when you are not up to doing much at all. On the good days it is important to do first the things that most need doing, because even on those days you will not be able to do all that you can when well. You will still tire easily and lose concentration before you have got through everything you had hoped to do.

It is also important not to utterly exhaust yourself. Work up to a reasonably comfortable limit, but do not push yourself beyond that limit. Constant pushing will drain your energy. A steady rhythm of activity and rest, short cycles of activity followed by longer ones of rest, will help you to recharge your low batteries so that they never get completely flat.

Making progress

Remember the mighty Euphrates river we looked at yesterday, and how it was divided into seven streams to enable the people to tackle a portion at a time. Seven streams means there were six islands between them, places on which to rest. Trust yourself to know when it is the right time for you to take a breather, to rest awhile in order to gather your strength for the next phase.

Progress does not come from pushing yourself to the limit all the time. It comes from a rhythm of effort, and ceasing from effort. When the disciples had had a busy time and were surrounded by people making more demands on them, Jesus took them to a quiet place with Himself for some rest. He did not say, "Go, and I will carry on here." That would have left them feeling very guilty and inadequate. No, the invitational command was *"Come with me ... and get some rest."* If you are wise you will accept the invitation gladly, and obey the command promptly.

> **"There is a time for everything, and a season for every activity under heaven."** Ecclesiastes 3:1

Press on

Recovery from depression is very like climbing a sand dune. Three strides up are inevitably followed by slipping back one or two paces. Progress is slow. The strategy is to pause when necessary, recover breath, and then press on. You may have slipped back one or two paces, but you had made three upward ones. There is a small net gain. At first it seems imperceptible, but each little gain accumulates.

That slippage as you climb the sand dune of recovery from depression is always disappointing, even when you know it is utterly normal and to be expected. You may not notice the gains you achieve when your goal, to the top of the sand dune, seems such a long way off. If you keep going you will be able to see that the bottom of the pit is getting further away, and so the top must be getting nearer. You are making progress. Keep up the rhythm of activity and rest, short cycles of activity followed by longer ones of rest.

For reflection and action:

- Maintain the rhythm of rest following activity.
- Push yourself, but not beyond your limit.
- Obey Jesus' invitation to "Come with me ... and get some rest."

Emotional Roller-Coaster

No wonder Elijah wanted to die. He was physically, mentally, emotionally and spiritually spent, depleted of all reserves. He had come through three years of drought that resulted in a famine, then he had a long period of playing cat and mouse with King Ahab. Finally he brought about a very public confrontation between himself as the lone representative of the Lord, and all the opposition, the four hundred and fifty prophets from the camp of Baal.

His prayer was answered. He then challenged the king to get himself down from the mountain and back home before he got stuck in the mud. In faith he prophesied torrential rain, despite a cloudless sky. He now had a nerve-racking wait during which he probably wondered whether he'd heard the word of the Lord correctly.

Complete exhaustion

Six times Elijah sent his servant to the top of the mountain to scan the horizon for any sign of the rain he had so confidently forecast. And there was none. On the seventh look-out trip there was just one small cloud, by which time Elijah was completely exhausted. His faith had been vindicated when his offering was accepted, then it was severely tried during that long, nail-biting wait under a relentlessly clear sky.

Sometimes he couldn't even look at it, he just sat with his head between his knees, too exhausted to pray, or do anything at all. He knew the roller-coaster of emotional exhilaration followed by that stamina-sapping hiatus, and to cap it all there was a price on his head again.

He was scared and he wanted to die.

> " 'I have had enough, Lord' " [Elijah said.] 'Take my life; I am no better than my ancestors.' Then he ... fell asleep ... an angel touched him and said, 'Get up and eat, for the journey is too much for you.' " 1 Kings 19:4–7

God understands completely

It is always so encouraging to me to see how God dealt with him in his extremity. There was no hint of reproach for his request to die, but total understanding of the state he was in. An angel was dispatched to see that his needs were met. He was not given an injection of courage, nor a homily to restore his faith. He was supplied with newly-baked bread, and fresh water.

After eating and drinking what was provided, he just lay down and fell asleep again, he was that tired. And God repeated the prescription. A repeat prescription is always a sign that the medicine is essential. Again an angel provided newly-baked bread for him to eat and fresh water for him to drink, and woke him up saying, *"Get up and eat for the journey is too much for you"* (v.7).

If you are exhausted, anxious and depressed, see that you take sufficient food and adequate rest. Do not try to continue the journey until you are both nourished enough and rested enough to tackle the next phase. Stay where you are until some strength returns. God fully understands.

For reflection and action:

- *God understands the state you are in.*
- *Look after your basic needs. See that you sleep, and eat.*
- *Stay where you are until strength returns.*

Surprises

I wonder if you have ever felt like Jeremiah sometimes did. During one especially difficult period he let rip and cursed the day he was born. He found it was a release to give expression to the utter weariness of being so relentlessly ground down. Expressing his frustration and his anger with God for putting him in such a predicament helped him to see his situation in perspective.

"But the Lord is with me"

He did not like the consequences of what he was asked to do, but when he had given expression to his turmoil and his despair he was able to say, "*to you I have committed my cause*" (Jeremiah 20:12). When he looked from his suffering to the God who called his life into being, he was able to draw strength and carry on. Although his life had turned into a gruelling test of endurance he was able to say, "*But the Lord is with me*" (Jeremiah 20:11). It was remembering that fact, that solid fact, that enabled him to carry on until there was some lessening of the load he carried.

At one time he determined to say nothing, to keep his head down and remain silent, but he realised this actually made him feel worse. It felt like a burning fire that was shut up in his bones and he was weary of holding it in. Giving expression to his pent-up feelings of alienation, isolation, anger and despair brought some relief, and renewed hope.

The person with whom you can always talk out your most sensitive issues is God Himself. Things you can hardly bear to admit to yourself are always safe to whisper in His ears. They are always perfectly safe in His heart, too. You are safe in His heart, and have a totally secure place there.

Talk to Him

Although God may surprise us, especially in His love and compassion for us and His open acceptance of us, whatever our state we will never take Him by surprise. Nothing we may hesitantly share with Him will shock Him. He knows what is going on. He cares deeply for each individual and wants each one of us to be secure enough in our relationship with Him that we can off-load on to Him. He really wants to bear our sorrows and share our burdens.

For reflection and action:

- *Expression of turmoil brings a better perspective.*
- *Keeping quiet increases the problem.*
- *God may surprise us. We do not surprise Him.*

River of Life

Part of the awfulness of depression is the inability to express what one is going through, which increases the sense of isolation, uselessness and despair. It is as though there is a communication barrier that one cannot push through, it takes too much energy. There seems to be a dam holding back the entire flow of the river of life and you become locked in on yourself.

Opening the sluice-gates

Pressure builds up behind the dam, and it takes a lot of energy to hold back all that life-force. Small wonder then that chronic tiredness of body and mind and deep weariness of soul are such a feature of depression. To alleviate this, and to prevent a further dangerous build-up of pressure behind the dam of silence, open the sluice-gate a little. Not a lot, but a little. Not all the time, but some of the time. Not to everyone, but to selected people, and especially to yourself. Gradually allow yourself to become aware of thoughts and feelings that have perhaps felt rather too threatening before. And most of all talk about this to God. Remind yourself of the love, tenderness and compassion of God, not just in theory, but specifically for you personally.

In that security allow yourself to begin to acknowledge the hurts, disappointments, fears, anger and whatever else you find within yourself. These are likely to be the accumulation of years, impressions gathered in various phases of your life so far, and they need to be expressed in order to let the river of life flow freely again. There is a saying that "impression without expression leads to depression". Expressing how you feel, and what you think, does not mean breaching the dam so that there is an uncontrollable rush of all that has been held back for so long. It requires a regulated opening of the sluice-gates so that the flow can get moving again in a life-enhancing way.

> **"When I was silent and still ... my anguish increased."**
> **Psalm 39:2**

Review your life

There is a time to speak out, and a time to keep silent. It is always time to speak out to God those thoughts and feelings you cannot share with others. Allow yourself to look over your life bit by bit with Him and to become aware of any areas of frustration. Are you a round peg trying to fill out a square hole, or a square peg trying to squash yourself into a round hole?

Review your life, your activities, relationships, responsibilities. Notice where it is overcrowded, and where there are uncomfortable gaps. If you feel trapped in one particular area, is it possible to compensate for this by finding more life, more enjoyment, more expression, more resourcing from another segment? Do you have any hobbies or interests? Perhaps you have put so much time and energy into your work that you have neglected the social and cultural aspects of life.

Ask the Lord of life to help you find small ways in which you can get going again.

For reflection and action:

- *Impression without expression leads to depression.*
- *There is a time to keep quiet, and a time to speak.*
- *It is always time to speak to God.*

A Passing Cloud

One summer when I was sitting on the English side of the River Severn sketching Chepstow Castle, I was entranced by the sunlight shining on the wet mud banks opposite me. As the tide went out, more and more mud was visible, more and more patterns of light and shade danced before me. Then a cloud covered the sun. The whole scene became dull and lifeless. The mud banks which had been so exciting to paint were now monochrome and featureless. They now appeared to be completely flattened, an uninteresting, uniform, murky shape and colour.

So often depression is like that, all the bounce and beauty, the interest and vitality, drains away from life. There is no longer any contrast, no highlights and entrancing shadows, just drab dreariness.

In my setting the sun had not gone away. It was still there shining as before and shedding its warmth from the sky, but a cloud had formed and obscured the sun, preventing its warmth from being felt below. As the sunlight could no longer get through and illuminate the scene before me, the prospect was totally uninteresting. The features themselves had not altered at all, but the light on them was now completely different. All I could do was to sit it out and get on with the routine things until the cloud had passed. So often we say we'll "wait for the sun to come out again" when the truth is that the sun never went in, and it never stopped shining. Clouds come between us and the sun, but the sun is there all the time shining with undimmed light and undiminished warmth, only we no longer receive that light and warmth.

Depression is like living under a large dark cloud that is so very slow to disperse. It feels as if we are stuck with it forever.

God does not change

It is always worth asking whether or not I have done anything to bring a cloud between me and the sun, between me and the Son of God. Once that question is asked, He will always graciously reveal any attitude or action that needs altering in order to shift the cloud and let the sun shine in again.

When no sin, no wrong-doing or thinking comes to mind, then the problem is likely to be in the climate, in my particular weather-zone, my depression, rather than in something of which I am guilty. Hang in there until it passes. It will shift, although it may take time. The natural history of the condition is that it will pass, and recovery will occur. The cloud will pass, the sun will shine again; warmth, interest and energy will come back.

While you are waiting for the cloud to pass, do only the routine things and leave the finishing touches, the highlights, the embellishments until light transforms your world again. The Son of God has not deserted you. Your illness obscures your appreciation of His presence, but He does not change. He shines on however big and dark and slow to move the cloud of depression might be.

For reflection and action:

- Wait for the cloud to pass. It will.
- Leave the finishing touches until the sun shines again.
- Ask yourself if you have contributed to the cloud in any way.

When Sleep Her Balm Denies

Waking up after just two or three hours sleep, often with a sense of foreboding, is one of the many distressing aspects of depression for large numbers of people. All that is worst in life seems exaggerated in the early hours of the morning. Since everyone else in the house or neighbourhood is likely to be asleep at the time, the sense of isolation and despair are particularly prominent at this time.

Try to focus on the Lord

Although you are wide awake you have probably found there is little hope of doing anything creative or constructive with the time. You may not be able to sustain it for long, but try to focus on one aspect of the Lord Jesus Christ. Every time your thoughts wander, as they will, gently bring them back to this task of fixing your mind on one aspect of the Lord. Ask Him to help you concentrate for a little longer each time.

You might find it helpful to recall some of your favourite Bible characters. Try going through the alphabet recalling what you know about someone, taking a name from each letter in turn. Reflect on what their story tells you about the character of God.

Or you might prefer to focus on your best-loved action stories: Noah building the ark, Moses leading the people across the Red Sea, Joshua encircling Jericho, Nehemiah rebuilding the walls of Jerusalem, Daniel in the lions' den. Just briefly reflect on what the story tells you about that person's relationship with God.

Do not try to dwell for long on any one event or person. Just recall it, savour it and give thanks to God that the story links you to Him. You will probably find that a particular subject helps to hold your attention one early morning but not another, so different approaches need to be tried. Here are some suggestions:

Storms in Scripture; people whose names God changed, and why; people God called, and those whose Name He called twice; the "*I ams*" of Christ; women in God's favour; the various names of God; soldiers of stature; people with special or unusual skills used by God.

Your mind will keep wandering off, but do not give up, and do not scold or berate yourself. The inability to concentrate is part of the depression. Remind yourself that the Lord understands this and responds to the desire of your heart to commune with Him even though you cannot sustain your part for long.

The important thing is not that you succeed in the task, but that your attention is continually being brought back to God. Your intention is to be receptive to Him even at what is probably your lowest-of-all low times.

For reflection and action:

- Focus on one aspect of God. Don't worry when your thoughts wander.
- The Lord understands your lack of concentration.
- The important thing is not that you succeed, but where you direct your attention.

Precious Tears

One day I watched a grandad with his young grandson. When the lad suddenly started to cry, grandad went to great lengths to try and stem the flow of the child's tears. That was a pity because it was done to ease the old man's distress rather than that of the youngster. If every important adult in that boy's life always rushed to divert him away from his tears he would learn to suppress his tears and in time might become unable to express, or even accept, the powerful feelings behind the outward show of tears.

Far better if grandad had cuddled him until the pain abated, then played with him as before. The boy needed to feel safe and secure as to the hurt he was experiencing. That way his confidence and his ability to handle the knocks of life would be built up.

During the early stages of depression it is not unusual for some people to become tearful. It is only one part of the general condition, but it is one which adds both embarrassment and unpredictability to an already uncomfortable state. This is just one feature of the illness which will disappear when recovery occurs.

As well as accepting tears as one feature of illness, it can also be important to consider whether there is any particular trigger for them. It may be an unresolved problem which rises to the surface again during illness. If a possible trigger can be detected, then the person needs to make a note of the problem area so that he can attend to it when recovery permits a more prolonged communing with God.

Other people find that when the depression deepens they are unable to cry at all. Sometimes they long for the release that crying can bring, but it is denied them. The ability to cry again, when there is appropriate cause and it is socially acceptable to do so, is for them a welcome sign of recovery.

> **"The Sovereign Lord will wipe away the tears from all faces; he will remove the disgrace of his people from all the earth."** Isaiah 25:8

He knows and cares

Whether the tears are ones of excess that signal the onset of illness, or the scant ones that herald recovery, or are just ordinary tears in ordinary times, they are all precious to God. He records them, and lists them on His scroll; they are never wasted. It is amazing to think that the Creator, the Sovereign of the Universe, knows and cares when a sparrow, just one small bird from a whole flock of similar birds, falls and dies. Not only that, but He also knows about, He counts and collects, each tear that you shed.

You and your concerns are that important to Him. Your sorrowing and your illness are felt by Him. Whether you feel His presence or not, He is with you in your sadness and sickness. You do not bear it alone.

He knew about your conception, and watched over your very earliest formation and growth in your mother's womb. He knows your physical, mental and emotional make-up – even the number of hairs that cover your head. Whether many or few, straight or curly, they are actually numbered.

For reflection and action:

- Consider whether there is a consistent trigger for your tears.
- All tears are precious to God.
- He knows and cares about your physical, mental and emotional state

Restored Years

When people are depressed it is as though they have been stripped bare by locusts. They have had all their current resources removed from them by the illness. On top of that the "locusts", that is to say the depression, often exposes hidden weaknesses. It is as though the depression eats through the veneer that has been covering up unresolved issues which are a hangover from years ago. These issues come to the surface again during illness, clamouring for some better, longer-lasting solution.

You may be having to cope with both the ravages of a depressive illness, and with what one friend of mine calls "the unpaid emotional bills from earlier years", all at the same time.

Unresolved emotional issues

For some people it is as though all the sorrow and anguish from a series of losses throughout their lives, the little ones as well as major bereavements, somehow become gathered together and get added to the present misery. For others it may be a broken relationship where the wound has continued to fester deep within the person, perhaps because at the time they could not manage to forgive either themselves or the other party, and so healing has not been possible. Or it may be a lingering resentment over that job they failed to get, or the time they were passed over for the expected promotion or some other desired role in life that has eluded them.

When this happens to you you may find yourself identifying with the author of Lamentations when he wrote "*I have been deprived of peace; I have forgotten what prosperity is. So I say 'My splendour is gone and all that I had hoped from the Lord ... my soul is downcast within me'*" (3:18,20).

> **"I will repay you for the years the locusts have eaten ... you will praise the name of the Lord your God, who has worked wonders for you."**
> **Joel 2:25, 26**

The compassionate Father

It is important to be specific about those things you had hoped for, and which were either never quite within your grasp, or which were taken from you. Only when you identify the root of your bitterness or resentment can you take the matter fully to the Lord. And when you do so, remember He is waiting to receive you with open arms, like the father whose son spent all his inheritance on selfish wrong living. When that youth was totally destitute he set out for home again intending to ask for a servant's lot. When he was part-way home he found that his father was scanning the horizon; waiting, longing, yearning for his return. When he came the father threw a party.

The years that the locusts had eaten were indeed fully restored.

The author of Lamentations continues the words we read earlier by saying, *"Yet this I call to mind and therefore I have hope: Because of the Lord's great love we are not consumed, for his compassions never fail"* (Lamentations 3:21,22).

For reflection and action:

* *Addressing problems as they surface is healing.*
* *The Father waits for you with open arms.*
* *His compassions never fail.*

Oscillating

No one feels joyful when they are depressed, and yet by focusing on the fact of being "in Christ" we can rejoice. Our ability to rejoice does not depend on our circumstances, and it is not an emotional state. It does not depend on our well-being, or on our health, or on our moods, or on any feelings at all. It depends solely on life being dependent on Christ, on the fact of being alive in Christ, of my life and your life being "*hidden with Christ in God*" (Colossians 3:3).

We do not rejoice in a vacuum, we can only rejoice in the Lord. And when we rejoice in the Lord we are told to do so constantly, always, whatever the circumstances. There are no off-days, and no days off, concerning Christian rejoicing.

Focus on the heavenly realm

This does not mean that we are to deny pain and suffering, but that rejoicing *in the Lord* goes beyond our temporal state and is a matter of the spirit. Rejoicing in the Lord is truly independent of my state of mind, body or emotions; it is in a different realm altogether. It has to do with living as a spiritual being in a spiritual plane at one and the same time as being fully aware of my suffering, and of other people's afflictions.

We can be very sad, and appropriately so, because of any number of circumstances and yet at one and the same time we also rejoice in the hope of the glory of God (Romans 5:2). These are not either/or situations but a both/and phenomenon. We can be sad, even depressed, and yet rejoice in the Lord.

We can be fully aware of what is happening in our humanity, and at the same time be even more aware of rejoicing in God. It is a question of where the focus is. Our attention will of course oscillate between the two realms. Often it will seem to be pegged down in our human suffering, but our focus can still remain in the heavenlies, on our Saviour and our God.

"I will rejoice"

An amazing picture is recorded in Habakkuk 3:17. "*Though the fig tree does not bud and there are no grapes on the vines, though the olive crop fails and the fields produce no food, though there are no sheep in the pen and no cattle in the stalls, yet will I rejoice in the Lord, I will be joyful in God my Saviour.*"

That is so often what depression feels like – somehow being stripped bare and rendered totally unproductive. Not just one crop has ceased, all have failed. There is no sustenance for man or beast, and all the animals have died off. Depression can feel like that, as though one has died inside. Yet I will rejoice!

Impossible! Improbable? Not "*in the Lord*".

For reflection and action:

- Rejoice in the Lord.
- Focus in the heavenlies; not on humanness.
- Accept the both/and state of depression and rejoice in the Lord.

A New Thing

There is a time to remember, and a time to forget. Remember there is light at the end of the tunnel. God has promised to carry you in the roughest places and then set your feet on firm, solid rock.

Remember God's promises

Remember Brother Lawrence, as conscious of God in his noisy kitchen as during times set aside for prayer. And my friend in the dried-up river bed, finding strength to continue when she relied fully on God, and found him fully reliable.

Do remember to be kind to yourself, and to forgive yourself as Christ forgives you. And that there is a time to forget; forget the incident you have forgiven.

Remember that God holds you by your hand and will never forsake you. If you fall it isn't fatal! He will help you up. When you come to the end of your resources, He is at the other end.

Winter does pass. The log-jam can be shifted by a prod from the logger, the Holy Spirit.

When you want to run away, check your relationship with God. Seek to experience His love for you, as well as knowing about Him with your head.

Remember you will never be exposed to more than you can bear. When life seems out of control there is always an escape road, and it is called the "Looking to Jesus" road.

However bad the depression, remind yourself that you will not drown in it, or be snuffed out by it. God knows you are a breakable clay jar in which He has chosen to reside. He has even engraved you on the palm of His hand.

The God of hope deals with obstacles in different ways at different times. Our part is to take one step at a time. Sometimes it will be like going up sand hills, three steps upward then slipping back two, but keep going and you get there eventually.

Look after yourself

When on an emotional roller-coaster, look after your basic needs; eat and rest before continuing your journey. God may surprise you in the provision He makes for you, but your secrets will never surprise Him. Speak out to Him. Open the sluice-gates a little to relieve the pressure that's built up behind the dam of silence.

Clouds do pass, and sunshine will brighten your landscape again; God has not deserted you. Recalling one fact about Him, or His servants, or their stories, may be helpful on wakeful nights.

When tears come don't staunch them, they are a safety valve and precious to God. Times of depression are not wasted, He will use what you learn from them to restore the years the locust has eaten.

He will cause you to rejoice. He is doing a whole new thing in your life, so that which was desert is now opened up, and what was wasteland becomes productive.

For reflection and action:

- *Forget what you have forgiven.*
- *Don't dwell on past hurts. Deal with them and move on.*
- *Live out the new thing God is doing in you.*

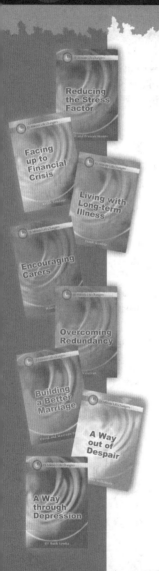